# SEX

BOING! BOING! BOING!

# BY ALLAN PLENDERLEITH

**R**
RAVETTE PUBLISHING

First published in 2001
Reprinted in 2003
Ravette Publishing Limited
Unit 3, Tristar Centre
Star Road, Partridge Green
West Sussex RH13 8RA

Printed in Malta by Gutenberg Press

ISBN: 1 84161 095 X

NEVER BLOW OFF
WHILE DOING THE
DOGGY POSITION.

JEFF TRIES TO CONVINCE THE POLICEMAN THAT THESE ARE, IN FACT, AIRBAGS.

MAUDE SHOWS
JEFF HER
HAIRY RING.

# JEFF KNEW HE HAD TO HAVE SEX – AND SOON!

HAVING RAN OUT
OF CONDOMS,
JEFF OPTS FOR
PLAN B.

MAUDE HAD
ACTUALLY ASKED
JEFF TO DO
SOMETHING KINKY
IN BED.

JEFF KNOWS HOW
TO REALLY
SATISFY A
WOMAN IN BED.

JEFF DISCOVERS
THE PERILS OF
HAVING A WOMAN
WITH BIG BOOBS.

WHEN JEFF SAID HE WANTED TO 'GO INTO THE BIG BROWN TUNNEL OF LOVE', MAUDE WAS RELIEVED TO DISCOVER IT WASN'T A METAPHOR.

JEFF HAD HEARD
WOMEN LIKE MEN
WITH BIG KNOBS.

JEFF KNOWS TO
ALWAYS SPEND
HOURS ON
FOREPLAY.

SOMEHOW, DURING THEIR LOVE-MAKING, LILY AND ALF BECOME ENTANGLED.

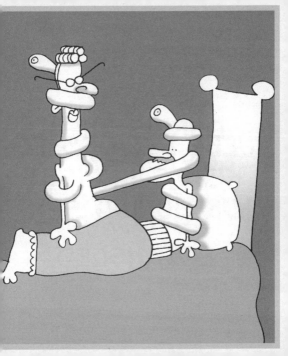

JEFF DECIDES TO
KEEP THE LIGHT
ON DURING SEX.

DUG'S WISH
TO GET A
LITTLE HEAD
COMES TRUE.

MAUDE PROMISED
NEXT TIME SHE
WOULDN'T LET
HER BOOBS
BOUNCE AROUND
SO MUCH DURING
SEX.

ED LOVES A GIRL
WITH BIG BOOBS.

JEFF'S VISIT TO A POLE DANCING CLUB WAS NOT WHAT HE EXPECTED.

MAUDE HAD HER
OWN SUBTLE WAY
OF TELLING JEFF
SHE WAS IN THE
MOOD.

FINALLY, JEFF
REMOVES
MAUDE'S BRA.

MAUDE
WONDERED IF SHE
HAD THAT
'JUST HAD SEX'
LOOK.

THAT CONDOM
THE CAT
SWALLOWED
LAST WEEK
FINALLY MAKES
AN APPEARANCE.

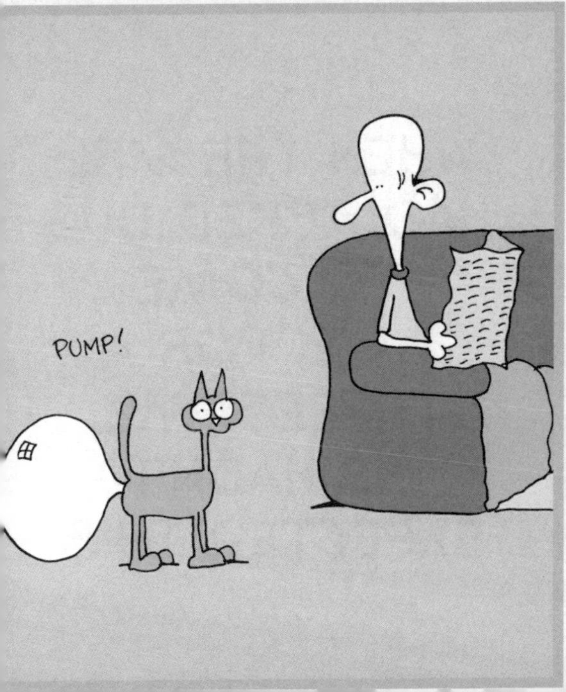
PUMP!

WHEN THE GIRL HAD ASKED DUG TO COME BACK FOR A THREESOME, HE HADN'T EXPECTED THIS.

FOR SOME
REASON,
BERTY BIG NOSE
ALWAYS SEEMED
TO HAVE TWO
GIRLFRIENDS.

IN THE MORNING,
DUG REALISES
HE SHOULDN'T
HAVE SLEPT WITH
HIS HEAD IN
BARBARA'S CHEST.

MAUDE'S DATE LOOKED COMPLETELY DIFFERENT IN THE MORNING – AND HAD SUCH BAD BREATH!

SUDDENLY,
DURING HER
SEXY DANCE,
MAUDE'S
SUSPENDERS
SNAP.

MAUDE ALWAYS
GOES FOR THE
MAN WITH THE
BIGGEST DONG.

MAUDE
DISCOVERS WHY
'FLAGPOLE PETE'
IS SO CALLED.

TO GIVE THE
ILLUSION OF AN
ACTIVE SEX LIFE,
SIMPLY KNOCK
HOLES BEHIND
YOUR HEADBOARD!

# NEVER BURP WHILE SNOGGING.

MAUDE TRIES
OUT A NEW
PERFUME THAT'S
IRRESISTIBLE
TO MEN.

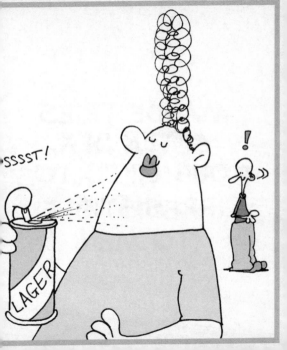

AFTER SEX,
DUG LIKES TO
LIGHT UP.

AS HE ENTERED
THE ROOM
UNEXPECTEDLY,
JEFF HAD THE
FEELING HIS
PARENTS HAD
BEEN UP TO
SOMETHING.

SUZY WOULDN'T KISS ED BECAUSE HE HAD MINT BREATH.

DUG'S DATE WITH 'BARBARA' WAS GOING GREAT, UNTIL THE TAXI LIGHTS SHONE THROUGH HER DRESS.

ED DISCOVERS
FLUFFY IS NOT A
TRUE BLONDE.

WHILE MAUDE SNEAKED HOME FROM WORK FOR A QUICKIE, HER CLEVER DECOY IS RUMBLED.

ED LEARNS
THE PERILS OF
SHAGGING THE
SOFA.

USING NOTHING MORE THAN AN UNCOOKED SAUSAGE, JEFF SHOCKS MAUDE WITH HIS 'WILLY SEVERED BY THE ZIP' TRICK.

SADLY, JEFF AND MAUDE REALISED TOO LATE THAT, DURING THEIR RAMPANT PASSIONATE BOUNCING, THE DOG WAS UNDER THE BED.

UH OH! DUG WAS SURE BRENDA HAD SAID SHE WAS ON THE PILL.

ALWAYS
DOUBLE-CHECK
THAT SEXUAL
AIDS ARE
REMOVED AFTER
USE.

Other **ODD SQUAD** titles available...

The Odd Squad's Little Book of ... series

| | ISBN | Price |
|---|---|---|
| Men | 1 84161 093 3 | £2.50 |
| Booze | 1 84161 138 7 | £2.50 |
| Women | 1 84161 094 1 | £2.50 |
| Poo | 1 84161 096 8 | £2.50 |
| X-Rated Cartoons | 1 84161 141 7 | £2.50 |
| Pumping | 1 84161 140 9 | £2.50 |
| Oldies | 1 84161 139 5 | £2.50 |

| | | |
|---|---|---|
| The REAL Kama Sutra | 1 84161 103 4 | £3.99 |
| The Odd Squad - Vol 1 | 1 85304 936 0 | £3.99 |
| The Odd Squad's Big Poo Handbook | 1 84161 168 9 | £7.99 |
| The Odd Squad Butt Naked | 1 84161 190 5 | £3.99 |

Ordering.. Please send a cheque/postal order in £ sterling, made
payable to 'Ravette Publishing Ltd' for the cover price
of the book/s and allow the following for postage and packing..

| | |
|---|---|
| UK & BFPO | 50p for the first book & 30p per book thereafter |
| Europe & Eire | £1.00 for the first book & 50p per book thereafter |
| Rest of the world | £1.80 for the first book & 80p per book thereafter |

Ravette Publishing Ltd.
Unit 3, Tristar Centre, Star Road, Partridge Green, West Sussex RH13 8RA